CU00869329

Out of Control

By Marcus Talese

Chrome Magnum Force

Black, back against the wall, you free fall into the pits of the unknown. Kick starting the day by screaming sounds of insanity as you wake up in your bedroom. A holy roller reaches the point of no return.

Driving like a speed demon shot straight out of hell, you form a thousand grins on your face. Take on the power and channel it straight into the big block engine of an ultimate death machine with four wheels!

Fuck like the animals that we really are without a care in the world. Keep breaking the laws as the government keeps making an endless amount of new ones. Squeeze out the last and final drop of goodness because everyone is full of bullshit anyway.

Don't take things to seriously for life itself is the world's biggest fucking joke! Why be so nice to them all? There's really no point anyway. So smash, crack and split that motherfucker's skull wide open with the power of the cold hard steel from a chrome magnum force!

1/6/20

Practice and Preach

It's so fucking easy to criticize everyone; it's so easy to enforce on how things should be. That's right point the fucking finger at the unknown and what you believe is evil. God forbid if you make one single mistake. But criticize the rest of the world!

Push him back into the corner. Beat that motherfucker within an inch of his life. Force your hand into that fuck nut and turn him into your puppet! He or she doesn't need their own thoughts or even a dream to go after! So go ahead pull the strings and force your commands. But at the same time remember all of the promises you and the rest of the assholes told us.

I'll be there for you, I'll never let you down, I'll show up this time, not to worry that evil fuck is gone, you can count on me, I fucking promise. Kiss my fucking ass! Too many people in this world are nothing but bullshit artists.

But it's so easy to criticize isn't it. Practice what you preach! Keep your word no matter what. Allow them to chase their dreams especially if it is something positive. You'll never know what that person can become in this world filled with false promises.

1/6/20

A Hole in the Wall

Small, dirty, but this place has character in its own unique way. "Would you like some coffee dear"? The waitress asks with a crack toothed grin on her 58 year old face!

The cook is in the back making sloop that only tastes just good enough to fill you up. However the liquor is clean, strong and will forever be cheap.

Truckers, drifters, slack jaw locals, hippies and sex machines all gather here to call this place home. When there is nothing to do and no place to go, this hole in the wall will always be open.

Snorting fat lines of cocaine in the bathroom, smoking joints outside the back door, drinking cheap booze in the kitchen and tripping on the liquid goodness as you wait on the tables is a way of life.

Fueled by the stress of life these workaholics need a place to eat and drink. Late night and early morning strippers come to conquer with loudness and tits shaking everywhere!

There is nothing like it in this world. Without a doubt everyone on this planet loves this hole in the wall!

1/12/20

Nightmares and Dreams

The nightmare is finally over! All that has haunted me in the past is done and over with. There is nothing holding me back from being happy, doing what I want within reason but most of all working towards the dream.

Roughing it out of the car has its ups and downs but most of all I have complete freedom. Running free to wherever I want to go. I must push the limits at the same time adapting to everything as I take things day by day.

I never wanted to become a great writer of perfection. I want to become one of the most insane writers of all time! The reason why is because there are too many books, stories, poems out there putting people to sleep. Fuck that bullshit! I want to shock and grab a hold of the readers out there in the world and give them entertainment for their minds. I will never stop flooding the world with my writing.

The nightmares are over with. It's now time to put in the work step by step and live the dream.

1/12/20

INK

Squeeze those tits of yours as the eye quakes start to begin! Your eyes roll back into your skull releasing your soul, kind of like blunt smoke rising into the heavens above!

All week long the stress has been building up and it's Friday night. You scream at the top of your lungs "Fuck it all I want the alcohol"! Tripping your face into the vortex you watch the ink on someone's tattoo covered body moving, shifting, expanding, melting and moving all around.

Unleash the pain. Don't let the demons get to you. Release all of the negatives. It does us no good. Breathe through your pores and take in all of that energized power. Consume the five gram heroic dose. Jump in the river and swim to the edge of a waterfall then jump off into a free fall.

Rage through the crowd head banging around! 1500 horsepower as you shift into sixth gear of the Ferrari Enzo. Two million watts of bass blasting out your ear drums making your ears bleed.

This is what Ink means to me. Infinite Non Stopping Killing Machine!

1/12/20

Metal

Bone crunching sounds as the metals collide together! Twisting the steel and molding it into a new creation. The cast iron block is completely renovated like new and ready to be reinstalled into an old Trans AM.

A steel sledge hammer with a rubber grip smashes through the concrete making that beautiful sound to past time. Cooper wire transformed into a fucking master piece of art work. A samurai cleans his sword after a blood bath massacre from killing over a thousand of his enemies

Sharpen those knives for they are looking a little bit dull. A wrecking ball made of iron smashes through the brick walls destroying the old in order to rebuild the new!

A steel cage is built into the frame of a 2013 850 horsepower Shelby Cobra super snake to keep the driver safe. Just in case a catastrophic, mind blowing cluster fuck of a train wreck happens. For example, the driver takes a turn to hard and the car starts rolling over and over again. I bet my last fucking dollar that driver would be praying and thanking God for the steel roll cage to save his or her life!

The double bass on a drum set is going faster than lightning strikes creating sounds of thunder! Meanwhile the bass and electric guitars are putting out heavy sounds from the power chords.

Ultimate power from the God's creating these sounds and use for the metal means this. The metal is back and it's here to stay!

1/15/20

Rampage

Three billion guns are loaded ready to take aim at us all! A counter strike against all odds creating a rapid fire to protect operation front line must happen. We must take full action and terminate the insane of this world!

The great and ultimate death machine has now become complete and fully operational. No time to waste! Bring the death machine to the front line. The troops need back up now!

Mass panic over comes the enemy as they finally see this death machine within their sight. Rampage is the name of this monster of a machine standing over ten thousand feet tall. Its armor is indestructible with a hundred billion cannons locked and loaded along with millions of rocket launchers. And will throw in a couple of flame throwers on there.

An endless amount of ammunition and fuel makes this juggernaut not only impressive but completely unstoppable! Unleashing its wrath upon the enemy as they run in fear and horror but it's too late. Even though there are three billion of them still this is no match for Rampage the ultimate death machine!

Rockets and cannon blasts hitting the ground creating massive explosions as the enemies body parts splatter all around. This behemoth of steel has the enemy running for their lives. Nothing to fear now for rampage the ultimate death machine will win this war!

Without warning the enemy brings out their own death machine. But it's no match for the almighty rampage! Finally the ultimate weapon from rampage comes out!

A lazar cannon forms from its chest and blasts a supersonic heat wave that instantaneously annihilating this machine. Plus killing all the enemy soldiers behind that piece of shit they call a death machine.

As Rampage continues to kill and destroy quickly in massive amounts, finally the war is coming to an end. Nothing and I mean fucking nothing stops rampage the ultimate death machine.

1/20/20

Jack Knife

Sliding out of control! This big rig starts to jack knife down the highway in the Rocky Mountains covered in snow. At the same time this truck dangerously hydro planes as the driver tries to regains control. Sweating bullets and dam near having a heart attack the driver regains control of his truck and yet there are still more dangerous obstacles straight ahead.

God help this soul for he has a long way down the mountain during this Colorado blizzard of a storm. Giant boulders rolling off the mountain and across the highway! "Fuck it, here we go"! The driver yells out and lights up a cigar with a zippo lighter using one hand. Thank the good lord nobody is on this highway at 2:30am. For this would definitely become a death trap and the body count would rise!

Quickly the driver drops it into a lower gear as the cigar smoke flies out the side of the cracked window. He dodges two boulders by steering to the left and then back to the right. The driver is dam lucky he put on the snow chains before driving.

The hope he's been looking for is a mile ahead. "Fuck yes"! The driver yells out. The local truck stop and tavern is in his sight. Bam, the driver hits the brakes and dam near pisses himself. For a bigfoot runs across the highway giving the driver the middle finger before he jums into the woods.

The driver and his truck pull into the truck stop and a sigh of fucking relief overcomes him. Mission accomplished and now it's time for a drink!

1/22/20

A Beautiful Master Piece

Hopefully you all have heard of the famous painter Bob Ross. This man was one of the happiest human beings that ever lived. Every day Bob would wake up with a smile on his face, smoking cannabis and eating Psilocybin mushrooms to expand his hippie mind. Now Bob is ready to start the day and paint another mountain or a waterfall. This man accomplished a lot of great things in his life.

But what if Bob turned to the dark side of life? What if Mr. Ross started smoking crystal meth and power drinking cheap potato vodka? Then this man starts painting horrific satanic images of demons ripping people's guts out and drinking their blood on a six foot canvas?

As Bob's eyes are now blood shot red and wide open from smoking meth, he comes up with a new creative idea of putting the last touches on his latest painting. So Mr. Ross commands his assistant who is a twenty one year old blonde servant with huge tits and her long hair in a pony tail.

Bob orders his servant to get on her hands and knees right in front of the canvas. Then he tilts her head back with a black choke collar the servant wearing tightly around her neck.

She obeys his command as Bob turns into a raging speed demon by taking another drag from his crystal meth pipe. Then he chugs four shots of vodka and now his dick is rock hard and ready!

Quickly Bob grabs a bottle of baby oil and pours a good amount straight into her asshole getting her ready for the fuck of her life! Then Mr. Ross enforces his dick into her asshole and she lets out a horrifying scream but at the same time takes it like a champ. This was the whole reason why Bob hired her. Not to worry and have no fear Mr. Ross is paying her with cash and long shots of pure adrenaline!

After five minutes of painfully pounding her little asshole like a crystal meth fuel injected jack hammer, Bob drains his hairy nut sack into her bleeding asshole. Without any warning Bob Ross then takes out a 44 magnum and puts it to the back of her head as he holds onto her choke collar

Bam! Bob fires a shot into the back of her cranium now there's blood, brain and skull matter splattered all over the canvas creating the finishing touches to this horrific master piece. Bob then takes out his one eyed monster covered in her blood. And now Bob's dick looks like Jason Voorhees machete that just killed a dozen people.

Mr. Ross then turns and looks into the camera with blood shot eyes of the insane and says "Ladies and gentlemen this completes our beautiful master piece for today"!

Now I will admit this is a tit bit off the wall bat shit crazy! And even as I think to myself my God this is fucking horrible! The world needs the original Bob to go back to smoking cannabis and eating psilocybin mushrooms and titty fucking his beautiful wife! That's what we need. This is what the world needs. Bob must to go back to painting beautiful scenery like the mountains, winter wonderlands and beaches. That's the Bob Ross the world loves. That super friendly hippie is what we all need in our everyday lives!

It's always good to think about positive things, like two perfect lesbians juggling a red jolly rancher with their tongues. Or winning five million dollars off of one mega millions scratch off ticket. Now this sounds more like a beautiful master piece to me. Doesn't that sound a lot better?

God I love women! Especially the ones that always say yes and don't bitch or complain too much. But I also love these ladies with tattoos all over their faces. Tattoos like high as fuck, hello kitty and fuck this job. Now that's a lady I can definitely fall in love with!

Another one that captures my interest is a woman breast feeding her seventh child while rolling up a blunt with one hand. Then she looks over at her fourteen year old child and screams at him. "Put my motherfucking 40 back or I'll rip your arm off and beat your ass with the bloody stump"!

At the same time she has a Newport 100 hanging out of the side of her mouth!

Holy shitty titty yes! Now this is without a doubt a bitch made of gold. Oh God I will marry her right on the spot without thinking twice about it.

Now these alien abduction cases everyone has heard about where a human being is on an operating table as these grey aliens are performing tests on them. They also have highly advanced technology far beyond our understanding.

Their mind control can keep us physically paralyzed so we do not move a fucking muscle because we are consumed by fear and horror.

Now in my opinion with all of their technology and knowledge how do these aliens stop a human being from shitting themselves? I'm talking about violent and explosive liquid shitting all over the fucking place!

That's right you big headed ignorant motherfuckers! You didn't think of that one. Did you? Fuck no you didn't see that one coming you little intelligent assholes. And now who is going to clean up this splattered shit of mess that is now everywhere?

I can definitely tell you who is not going to clean it up, is that human being you have paralyzed on your operating table! Therefore you little grey God forsaken fuck nuts are going to clean up this human's shit. That's right have fucking fun with that!

Now to leave on a good note and make everything better I'm going to leave you with some words of wisdom. From the great mind of Bob Ross he would always say this. "Remember we never make mistakes. We make happy little accidents". Fuck yes! Then Bob would beat the little devil out of that paint brush!

I am Sleazy Talesezy and oh God in Heaven it feels great to be back!

2/15/20

Get Ready

Being shot straight out like a cannon ball with the force of a two ton nuclear war head. You fly through the air and fire up that pre roll with a wind proof lighter. Like a sloppy wet fuck you land on the bar sliding across it grabbing every free drink you can and at the same time you tip the bartender 100 grand!

Jumping into this customize race car you start it up and feeling the 400,000 horsepower under the hood. With the tires burning rubber and smoke firing out behind, you launch and drag race a mile reaching the finish line only in one second. Afterwards you yell out the window. "Fuck yes! Let's do it again"!

For you are the one. You are the hell rider. The one who can take on everything! You run through the fire of the dammed soaked in gasoline screaming out "Quick somebody, get me a fucking light"!

Take no shit. No pain can hurt you. Let go of the past and gain everything in front of you while you still can. With a jokers smile you take that one last drop of liquid in order to see insane melting things mixed with inner dimensional 3D images!

Without a second thought you jump off into the waters of perfection. When you come out you scream into the world "Get ready motherfuckers because a new legend is born"!

2/15/20

Not to Worry

You have both the red and the blue pill. Which one do you take? Fuck it, take them both and jump head first down the rabbit hole! It's the only way to find out the truth.

Colliding in between the physical and the dream worlds your 6th sense and third eye vision is forced into overdrive! This mind gripping experience will not only change your life but also how you look at everything.

Only one hour slips on by and the déjà vu starts as the separation beings. You can't tell if you really walking through these walls or are they shifting all around you? Now you see things that already happened but in different abstract ways. An over whelming feeling of panic strikes you quick, but yet you remember what you're really in for.

Taking a walk outside and seeing people walking toward and all around you. With no warning your now able to see with x ray vision, know every thought they make and can even look into their past.

But now the ground is starting to shift. The city is transforming into a jungle and at the same time a dog you had as pet ten years ago runs towards you. The truth hasn't come yet but it's getting closer.

Running through this neon jungle thinking about two things, what the hell is happening and I'm happy I took both the blue and the red pill. Pythons, jaguars, lemurs and insects are following your every move as you continue to pick up speed!

A split second later you're now running along the rings of Saturn. Jesus this is beyond the mind blowing madness of anything I could think of! Without any sound hundreds of UFO's appear performing maneuvers of intergalactic perfection!

The next thing you know you're being sucked backwards into a black hole. Traveling past the speed of light and shrinking into the negative in order to fit through it. Every cell in your body becomes electrified as you gain a power from the unknown!

This black hole now spits you out into another universe with planets, moons and stars, has never been seen before by any human being! But not to worry and have no fear. Just as long as you are still alive, you be fine.

2/18/20

Drop Kick

Fuck it! Break the ground. You have all the time in the world. Destroy the evil. Take the risk. Kill them all and execute the prisoners right now!

You have nothing to lose so why even wait half a second. You are far beyond the power of any god. Transform into the machine that will never stop and cannot be destroyed. Unleash the wrath of a million supernovas and disintegrate all of those evil politicians on earth into nothing!

It's ok to keep the madness going, just as long as the innocent survive. Obtain the acid rain and purify it so we can all live from it. Burn the stage by using 100,000 gallons of rubbing alcohol. Nobody needs to hear that controlling bullshit anyway.

Surf across the lake nice and smooth like glass as you try to balance both heaven and hell. Two seconds to think about tomorrow. A billion years into the future as a hundred pounds of

Psilocybin helps open your third eye in order to see what's coming ahead.

There's always a point to light up the darkness and use the fire as a weapon. Going off the top of my head as the debit disappears just like it was never there.

The head bangers will forever gather there because 500,000 watts of pure bass keeps them coming every year! What's insane about running through these padded rooms unlocking every door and screaming at the patients? "There's not a fucking thing wrong with you"!

For God sake these are good people with creative minds. That's all. There's nothing to worry about and nothing to fear. However we must not let them consume all of the world's drugs and alcohol. For the devil himself, just might get a tit bit worried!

Nose dive this 747 plane straight into the Atlantic Ocean. But just before the impact jump out with a parachute, sunglasses, a surf board and one cup of coffee. Those fifty foot waves look perfect to surf on. And I will kill you if you spill that cup of coffee!

Take a trip, show some kindness, take the longest piss of your life and have one shot for last call. Gather the troops; break the glass to escape the horror. Panic for time stops for on one, do a quadruple back flip off the diving board and land into a pool without water or perhaps will just fill it up with hydrofluoric acid. Let us flip a quarter on that one.

No matter how fucked up the day gets or how bored you are please read this a thousand times. But most of all! For god sake, run at full throttle and drop kick that demon straight through its motherfucking throat!

And just before you pass by that two horned fuck nut, take the last of his cash from the back pocket. Why you ask? Because fuck him, that's why! And now it's time to live life!

2/25/20

Take a Minute

Swimming towards the sunrise, you stop and float to take in this beautiful part of the world. However the sharks are now closing in. It's time to get your fucking ass back to the beach really quick!

Pure entertainment but extremely dangerous! To take a mouth full of ever clear bungee jump off a bridge and spit fire all the way down. A massive blast of subzero ice cubes falls into a containment holding one thousand gallons of grey goose vodka. At the end of this containment are a hundred straws for everyone to have a drink.

Take a minute, no time to rest, you're still alive, consume the good, drive the madness out of your minds, hydro plane across the sky, electrify your eyes, the time is now, fuck what happened yesterday because the future ahead is endless!

Hold back the hate, get rid of the fear, enforce the love, whiplash your head around in the crowd, do all that you can to contain this power! Fuck what you knew before. Now take on this new meaning of life and wisdom. Before death finally consumes and takes you to the next level!

Hold her up on your on your shoulders as she juggles fire at the same time snowboard down the Rocky Mountains. Do or die! Pulverize through the barriers of space and time. A fifty foot monster truck speeds through the city and breaks through the walls of rules and nonsense.

Take a thrill ride into the unknown. This rollercoaster drops and turns with supersonic G forces. Earthquakes are breaking the sound barriers. These tornados continue destroying all of the enemies of nuclear warfare. Millions of killer hornets swarm through the underground caves in the dark for they need no light to find their way.

Just take a minute and open your mind.

2/25/20

Overkill

Use a double barrel sawed off shotgun just to kill a fly. Swing that wrecking ball and take that bullies head off as the blood splatters off the top of his neck. Barely alive! But I'm not dead. Not yet anyways. Use the unlimited strength to break through ice to save a million lives.

Unload a thousand bullets into just one enemy then dump 100,000 gallons of sulfuric acid to complete the termination. Hammer the nail straight through the 2x4. Like a battering ram drop kick the door down. Grip the world by the throat and scream you will love me now!

The skin and eyes fly off his face as you yell at him with the sound of a supersonic force. Bang your head against the wall a hundred times to a bloody mess just to catch a buzz. A double blast of nitrous oxide pushes the Hennessey venom GT to 300mph!

Never hold back. Keep these thrill rides going to the maximum. Fuck it, overkill it!

2/25/20

A beautiful day in the neighborhood

It's 7am and the sun is out. But so is your neighbor next door who is drunk and sitting on his front steps. With a blank stare in his eyes your neighbor pisses his pants holding an almost empty bottle of old crow.

To your left another neighbor gets out of the cab wearing a short dress walking towards her house. Her husband comes out screaming "Where the hell have you been, you fucking whore"! The wife takes out a loaded 38 special, aims it at her husband and yells back "Get the fuck back in that house Gary"!

An unknown vehicle slowly drives down the street. This vehicle stops and the driver blasts the horn. The home owner opens the front door then the guns come out instantly to take aim and fire at this homeowner. Quickly he jumps back into the house to grab his rocket launcher. The car tries to get away but there's no point. Within seconds he takes aim and fires destroying the car in one massive explosion!

Perhaps this could have been a drug deal gone wrong! Or maybe they just didn't like each other. But who the fuck knows and who the fuck cares.

Running down the right side of the street is a ten point buck and closing in are four pit bulls and five great Danes! Within seconds they take down this huge buck. Ripping apart the stomach, legs and the throat as the buck screams in agony but thank god it's a quick death. Now some people would call this repulsive, violent, unnecessary and disgusting. As for me fuck it. I call it team work. However it's now breakfast for these dogs.

As you stand back and take in the moments drinking your coffee. You think to yourself this is what the world has become! Then a smile forums on your face as you say out loud "My god it's another beautiful day in the neighbor".

Now it's time to start the day!

2/27/20

Beyond Death

Your heart is racing but you smile like a mad man for the last thrill ride of your life. Running at full speed you feel the wind against your face as you run towards the cliff. Without hesitation and no going back, you jump off flying head fist with a smile on your face.

Only 5,000 feet to go until impact and you scream out "Fuck yes, bring it on death"! A split second after your skull hits the ground is the next second the soul breaker happens. Now you travel into warp speed into the spiritual realms.

Nightmarish images of sinister beings from hell torturing and ripping apart the souls of the dammed! The walls of hell fire are closing in all around you! No time to panic into suffocation. Nonetheless these demons are definitely coming for you.

Without warning a white light gaining strength and power emerges through the fires of the eternal damnation. Just before the hands of hell grabs a hold of your soul. The power of this light destroys half the realm of hell. Its power brings you in for protection and guidance.

An arch angel coming towards you, this being of light and endless positive energy shows you the meaning of life! You take a ride with her through the infinite heavens all around you. She shows you the glory and everything good about God's creation in the different realms and dimensions of the heavens.

Your soul feels electrified with unconditional love and understanding. The final step is the rebirth. The arch angel covers you in a golden light to create a new soul for the reincarnation you will become. Now the transformation is complete both the arch angle and God become one spiritual being and are ready to send you back to earth.

No sound, no sense of time, breaking the barriers of reality, opening up everything of existence, God spits you back out into the physical realm on earth. You started on one side of this planet and now from the bottom of the great oceans you rise.

With just enough push from God's incredible power you fly through the water towards the sky. But you are no longer in a human forum. Instead your new physical body is an eagle. You have become a new species of eagle, golden in color but with a giant wingspan.

Flying straight out of these waters with perfect forum you head to towards the sunrise. For a new day has risen and from beyond death a new life form lives on this planet.

God's power can come in many infinite mysterious ways. With no fear but only wisdom you fly across the earth. You now see this world in new, advanced, and perfect vision. There's nothing out there that can stop you. All the time in the world to travel the skies in pure freedom and a higher sense of everything!

Like a phoenix rising out from nothing. You fly straight into a new life. The time is now and the mission is clear to live life to the fullest no matter what's coming ahead.

Beyond motherfucking death!

3/3/20

Super Sonic

Blasting through inter dimensions of space and time. Traveling beyond the speed of light and pushing through the unknown. You have still have faith you can complete impossible mission! The ability to travel faster than any human being ever has! This is your mission.

A mind blowing amount of money was used to build this craft. It's the only one ever made, however was tested many times to perfection! It can with stand any amount of force, temperature and pressure.

Flying in and out of worms holes faster than any supersonic speeds! The ultimate adrenaline head rush of a thrill ride. All of your senses are in hyper sensitive mode but you have been training for this moment for the past four years.

Part of this mission is trying to find the edges of the universe. Quickly you enter another worm hole to travel faster, like skipping rocks through intergalactic space. A blast of solar wind knocks you off course and you crash into the side of a comet!

Not to worry for this craft was built to be indestructible! You won't even feel a minor whiplash. It only takes you seconds to regain control the craft but then you fly straight through the rest of the comet.

Faster than a blink of an eye you continue on your journey traveling at ridiculous speeds. Somewhere in the untouched parts of the universe you slow the craft at a cruising speed to witness a new planet quickly forming and being born.

3/8/20

Simple Minded Bullshit

"Get the fuck out of the way"! God in heaven I cannot stand it when people walk across the street slower than a snail stoned off of indica hash. All I'm trying to do is make a fucking right turn that's all!

You try to be nice. Trying to be a decent human being but most of these people are simple minded assholes. Sometimes when I open the door for them and it's usually the one's wearing Gucci and Armani, they never say thank you. Son of a bitch in hell I just feel like bending them over and smashing their skulls on a ledge made of brick and stone! Then I'll take that over priced Michael Kors bag and shove it straight up their fucking asshole!

Mr. and Mrs. know it all! No matter how many times you try to help them or explain things to them they never listen, however if a horrible disaster happens then the fucking light bulb lights up inside their heads. Now they get it. For some god awful reason now they understand! Nonetheless a tragedy has to happen in order for them to get the fucking point.

This reminds me of the old story of dead man's curve. Some people warned so many others. But they didn't listen and they didn't give a fuck. Obviously one day some dumb ass drove to fast on that curve. The vehicle runs off the road hitting a big oak tree and the mindless bastards die instantly on impact! Happy now.

If people would just listen to reason and basic logical thinking this world can become a great place.

Another thing that drives me beyond the level of bat shit crazy! Are the endless questions continuously coming nonstop from these destructive robots? What do these people do? Do they actually wake up in the morning and say to themselves in the mirror?

"Oh what the hell, I'll just go to the customer service counter and fuck up someone's day. Hold up the line on purpose with fifty people behind me. Then I'm going ask the same twenty questions over and over again like an out of control broken record. And yes I'm actually going to do this, simply because I have nothing better to do with my life. But to piss people off and make this world a living nightmarish hell"!

I mean honestly and I'm guessing there are actual human beings across the planet creating this madness towards hard working people just for the fucking fun of it.

Jesus, God in heaven can we please kill these demons and destroy the factories they were created in. Or at least beat the stupidity out of these evil, sinister human beings. Afterwards let us all force some intelligence straight down that fuck hole, they call a mouth.

I truly believe if we terminate all of this simple minded bullshit the world can become a better place. Thank you all and now it's time to have a cigarette. But before I go there's one last thing I have to say and explain.

Before God created light into existence, God yelled out to the stupid ignorance of this world. "Get the fuck out of the way"!

3/20/20

Spit Fire

Flames of the insane, a time to kill, but at least we now have the money. An endless amount of funds just to have fun! A violent tornado of destruction pulverizes the land. The body and mind are super jacked up with a mega shot of pure adrenaline!

Scream you motherfuckers and take no shit! Subzero blood but it's still running at the speed of light through you're veins. Spit the blue fire straight into an endless death. Bring life to new ideas into this highly advance technological world. Control the hate and uplift the weight of this planet. A fist of anger can break through all the walls of bullshit killing the lies.

Thick skin made of unbreakable stone. A wrecking machine slams these bodies through the sound barriers of steel and glass making an entertaining visual for the crowd. Born and bred to take on anything. Kill the evil that's destroying this country.

Highly intense lightening electrifying filling the dark skies and crashing into the ground creating havoc! Several ninjas running along the roof tops in stealth silence ready to complete the mission. A 1965 customized super snake launches from the starting line leaving the Veyron in the dust!

Transforming and morphing into a werewolf tearing apart a hundred ton tank like it was a tin can. Breaking bones and ripping the bad guy's arms out of their sockets like a heroic horror flick. Stampedes of mammoths are charging at full throttle breaking the ice behind them. The incredible cures the impossible and completes mission impossible.

A monster truck rampages through fire, ice, dark matter and acid rain. Making this beast looking brand new straight off a show room floor! Ten MC's spitting fire up on the stage driving the audience into a frenzy melting their eye balls off these teenage faces!

3/25/20

Sweetness

Sweeter than she looks and tastes even better! Transforming those psychotic white eyes into blood shot red of perfection to start the day. With a psychedelic liquid racing through her veins she still holds a smile of pure perfection no matter how extreme the pain!

With neon paint covering her entire body Miss Sweetness enters a room full of mirrors. Up top and all around the room are black strobe lights and four stripper poles filled with liquid purple lightening. She dances around swinging that hair of red fire. Creating supersonic trails head banging everywhere as she twists and turns in between these poles like an acrobatic goddess of madness.

Filling the air with love and violence she hovers above the ocean sitting Indian style releasing the chemicals from with inside her third eye. Not ready to die and too young to surrender she battles the evil ripping their throats out using speed demon cat like reflexes. And she does this all with a smile on her face as her eyes roll back into the depths of her skull.

She's comfortably lying on a long table with her hair stretched out the back while twenty lesbian strippers are putting on multi color cake icing from her neck to her toes. A midget clown is standing on a platform with a blunt hanging out of the side of his mouth. He watches these girls perfectly put this rainbow colored icing all over her body transforming Miss Sweetness into a human cake.

Ten lesbian strippers stand on each side of the table getting ready to win that prize! Whichever side licks this sweet lady clean wins her signature and a $1,000.00 gift card to her favorite cannabis dispensary.

Just before the race begins one girl places a cherry on this psychedelic goddess tongue to hold. And for fuck sake she better not drop that cherry! Or else that midget clown will flip her over and spank her sweet ass with two fly swatters. However it's hard to keep still and trying desperately not to laugh when there's twenty tongues licking you all over clean.

The midget clown aims his 38 special up in the air and says. "Get ready, set, and go"! He fires the gun and now it's time for dessert!

Inside this class room the silence is thick in the air. The teacher with eyes wide open asks this. "So class, what did we learn today"? "We will never piss off Miss Sweetness ever again". They reply back. "That's correct children"!

The next morning during the sunrise this goddess of sweet enlightenment and perfection walks outside on the balcony naked. With a two foot blunt in one hand and a lighter in another, she fires it up. After this sweet goddess inhales and exhales that thick white chronic smoke creating another massive cloud for the sky to hold. She releases a smile from eye to eye and says. "Good morning world. Now please get fucking ready for you will love me forever"!

3/9/20

Piss Drunk

The captain is drunk once again! He's still drinking those 16oz cans of IPA's at 9% alcohol. But his hands are steady as he grips the wheel with one hand and a can of piss in the other.

Out in the distance ahead is the great storm closing in. Of course this storm was darker than nights in hell! It filled the sky in horror as the captain's heart began beating faster. However within the depths of his mind he says to himself. "We can make it. We can take this bastard head on"!

So the captain of this boat grabs another ice cold can of IPA. Quickly he cracks it open and drinks half of the can in one sip to sharpen his sight and strengthen his spirit!

For hours on end this captain has been drinking. Yes! It is true that he is without a doubt now piss fucking drunk! "Brace yourselves fellas. We are going in"! The captain warns his crew and then empties the rest of the can straight into his alcoholic gut.

The waves are much higher than before. Lightning strikes are closer and all over the sea, for they are now inside the storm. The wave's crash and fly over this fishing boat as the captain steers and maneuvers avoiding any possibly for this ship to tip over.

Have no fear, for this captain is not only a professional. Yes indeed he is also a professional drunk! He steers this ship perfectly with his left hand and drinking another IPA that one of the crew members has handed him. But now this Captain filled with hate and anger towards this storm has got to take a filthy piss!

Wind, thunder, lightning and rain surround them all! How the captain has a steady grip on the wheel steering this fishing ship through these dark waters of hell!

As the captain's crew brace themselves from the impact of the waves, the captain yells out "Where's the coffee"? Then he slams back the rest of his beer down his throat. However, this man, this great leader can't take it anymore. Just before he pisses his pants, the captain cries out to his crew "Quick take the wheel"!

Two of his men grab a hold of the wheel and hang on for dear life! The captain opens the door while the howling winds and rain push the door open as the leader of this ship tries to hold his balance. This door is heavy but however with the captain's alcoholic strength, he slams the door with one hand.

Quickly this drunken leader of perfection slides to the edge of the ship grabbing a hold of the rope. The captain is soaked and wet from this monster of a storm! He pulls his dick out to take the piss of his life! As the captain drains his one eyed fat fuck; he leans back to let out a sigh of relief while the rain falls upon his face.

Without warning and just before the last two squirts of piss went flying out of the captain's dick hole. A fierce gust of wind from this storm purposely forces against the captain's back. Pushing him to hit the post with his gut and now the captain starts vomiting 40 ounces of high grade IPA.

Right after he finishes puking and pissing the captain turns to face the storm while white lightning crashes all around this poor bastard. This leader screams out "You fuck"! The captain lets this asshole of a storm know that he is the boss.

"I am the captain of this ship and nothing will stop me from completing my mission". This drunken leader screams at the dark skies filled with wrath and horror. With no time to waste, the captain slides to the door and opens it. "Quick, bring me the coffee"!

One of the captain's crew members hands him the old metal coffee pot with a tit bit of rust on the handle. The leader of this ship chugs the black coffee fast with a little spilling out of the side of his mouth. It looked the same as if the good captain was drooling in his sleep!

Now with a new mixture of high powered caffeine and quality alcohol, they both mix perfectly well in his gut. And now a great combination of violent madness fills the captain's mind with a new psycho driven power!

But not to worry and have no fear, for this man is a motherfucking professional! Right after the pot of coffee was empty; the captain throws it to the side hitting the wall before it lands on the floor.

Steady with his right hand this leader grabs another IPA and opens it with one hand. While his left hand steers this ship. "Hang the fuck on men"! The good captain alerts his crew. Their leader then forces the throttle to maximum capacity!

With another can of IPA in his hand, the captain takes a big old swig of beer as the ship reaches the top of this now fifty foot wave! The ship quickly slides straight down extremely fast but steady with the captain's control.

The leader of this ship knows exactly what he is doing. Not only did this man earn the rank of becoming a captain but he is without a doubt a professional drunk!

Finally the ship reaches the bottom of the wave. The captain with quick reflexes steers to the left but at the same time chugs the rest of his IPA. As he continues to steer the ship to the left and in between the upcoming waves, the captain throws the empty beer can over his shoulder.

With the swiftness this great leader grabs another can of IPA and opens it with one hand. Then he processes through these dark waters.

The ship is tilted on its side cursing along another monster wave. And now the crew is a tit bit worried. However the great captain of this ship has no fear! For his alcoholic soaked brain has the experience to maneuver their way out of hell!

Finally there's a light up ahead while white lightning still continues to strike the dark waters of the sea and all around them. The crew now has hope for the end of this horror is now in sight. Nonetheless the great captain knew all along they would make it. No matter what!

Forty five minutes later the waves have finally relaxed. The captain has finished eight more IPA'S within this amount of time. However the captain has no double vision and no cocaine to stay awake. Just a pure adrenaline, alcoholic, psycho driven running at the speed of holy fucking shit in his veins!

The storm is over. The crew is happy as the captain yells out mission accomplished! Now it's time to get the fuck to work and go fishing. But first the captain fires up a ten gram blunt for the victory is here!

"Get the hell over here quick men"! The great captain shares his mighty blunt with his crew. This great leader is never a greedy self centered fuck but cares for his crew and this ship!

Now it's back out on the hunt to catch as many fish, make a fuck ton of money while they still can. The future looks so bright for the captain, his crew and the ship.

5/2/20

RED

Quack the mother fuck out of that duck! It's time to slip and slide all up and down her giant tongue. Not to worry and have no fear, for her tongue will be forever wet for the whole world to have fun on. Fuck! It's fun for the whole family.

Ten thousand shots filled with adrenaline forced directly into your cerebral cortex, just to start the day. Take charge and order them to obey your every single command. A twin turbo forced inducted power trip! Win multi millions of dollars in Vegas so everything within your sight becomes free!

But for a limited time only kill them all! However do it with kindness and please put a smile on your face as the DMT trip takes over. Rip their fucking lungs out as the insanity builds up behind your pressurized eye sockets!

What? What the fuck do you want? Well all I need is just your soul! A quick and painless death turning the seas red, here comes the hammer head! Fuck the cocaine blood stain! Double inject a blast of nitrous oxide straight into your blood stream. It's ok and it's alright to scream! For now you're definitely ready to go for that Sunday drive in an all wheel drive twin turbo Dodge Viper. Please make sure to bring an extra bottle of nitrous, so you don't fall asleep behind the wheel.

A king cobra hypnotizes the crowd towering over them at a thousand feet tall. He licks his fangs with its purple blue tongue making a quick decision on who to strike at first!

Take what's yours and fuck the rest of them. A giant against all odds, so hang on for the threat is real. A battering ram breaking down the walls of greed! Far beyond a God, here comes the almighty with the original force!

Having a tight grip on a terrifying situation is always fun but only if you have complete control of its horror. A back breaking job taking you know where. But mother is sick and she needs her medication. Mother's mind can't handle the stress anymore for her last nerve is about ready to snap and break the fuck off!

Life itself is always continuously running towards death! Don't blink just yet because we were all born not yet ready to die. Dancing around on top of the razors edge piss drunk and not giving a flying fuck! However from down below thick white clouds of indica chronic smoke flies straight up to get you stoned and knock you off balance.

Get your little asses over here or I'll rip your arms off and beat you with the bloody stump! Like the grateful dead once said. I'll still your face right off your head!

There is no Hell without a heaven. Crucified for nothing, but give it time and I will rise again more powerful than ever before.

Just when you thought it couldn't get any better, the great one, the almighty! The Supreme Being takes those pure evil little Nazi bastards and shoves, forcing them into a giant wood chipper that's painted motherfucking RED!

2/27/20

The Restaurant

A family of five comes inside this fine establishment to have dinner. At the hibachi grill the chef is ready and excited to put on a show for this family and others. The wife is wearing a dress revealing a lot of cleavage while her giant tits jiggle around as she moves in her seat.

The chef gets too excited and accidently squirts hot oil that's on fire all over her monstrous tits as she screams in a panic and horror. Why? Because her motherfucking tits are on fire!

Immediately her husband stands up and screams at the chief. "You stupid fucking asshole, look what you did to my wife's tits"! Just before the chef could say sorry back the general manager comes up behind him and grabs the chief by the back of his throat.

The manager picks the chief up in mid air and slams him to the ground. "You're fucking fired! Get your shit! And get the fuck out of here"!

One hour later the chef walks down a dark alley drinking a fifth of cheap old crow. Walking sideways the chef sits down leaning his back up against a building. Quickly he takes out a thin rubber hose and wraps it around his arm. The chef then starts cooking the dark side of the spoon. Out comes the needle to complete the job!

After the hardcore injection this chef drops both of his arms with the needle still sticking out of his left arm. Out from the darkness and the fog a clown midget emerges smoking a Cuban cigar.

"Holy fuck buddy you don't look so good"! The clown says to him. The chef tries to respond but can only speak in a slurred gibberish with drool coming out of the side of his mouth.

"Don't worry about a fucking thing buddy; I'm going to help you out"! The clown says with the cigar in his hand and smoke coming out of his mouth.

Like an ultimate magic trick the clown pulls out from behind his back a syringe that's twice the size of him! The fluid inside this giant syringe is a mixture of pure adrenaline, serotonin and twenty drops of electrifying liquid heaven!

"Get ready here comes your medication"! The clown says to the chef and then jams this massive syringe into his neck. Thirty seconds later all of the fluid is flowing through the chef's blood stream.

Now this motherfucking processional is fully awake and ready to take on the world. Quickly the chef stands up and screams "Fuck yes! That hit the spot. "Thank you little boss man"! "Not a problem big guy". The clown replies back.

The chef is now off his ass and turns around facing the brick wall to take the filthiest piss of his life! Once the chef forced the last two squirts of piss out of the eye of his needle the clown was now ready to lead on!

"This way Mac, I'm taking to my favorite bath house called slippery sweetness". "Fuck that sounds like my kind of place"! The chef responds back. So the chef follows the little clown two blocks down as the cigar leaves a smoke trail behind them.

Finally they arrive at slippery sweetness. When inside this fine bath house it's painted black and red. The clown says to the head mistress. "Please give my friend here the works". "You got it boss"! The mistress says with a smile on her face as she opens up her pinky ring to take another bump of MDMA.

The chef is now inside a shower that can fit fifty of him with six of the mistress's finest girls.

Now the electrifying liquid running through his veins at the speed of light has reached its full potential.

"Fuck yes"! The chef screams as the visuals are now at its peak. Meanwhile his balls are being cleaned, his dick is getting sucked off and his hair is being washed as one of the ladies is standing on a step ladder washing his hair.

After the chef busts out cum from his nut sack four times covering all of these fine girls, he was ready for another wash and then a quick massage. The chef was a brand new man and ready to take on the world with a new uniform to wear at work!

Both the clown and the chef thank the great mistress for everything! "Here you go boys". The mistress hands them both two foot long joints with peyote in them. The chef and the clown light up the joints and then walk out the door. "Mistress, thank you again for everything"! Both said the clown & Chef.

After a twenty minute walk they arrived back at the restaurant. "Don't worry about a thing Mac I got you your old job back"! The clown says to the chef. "Boss I can never thank you enough for everything you have done for me"! "Anytime big guy, now get your hairy nut sack in there and make me fucking proud"! "Yes sir". The chef replies back to his little guardian angel.

Once the chef was back inside the restaurant the manager greeted him with open arms, like nothing ever fucking happened! "Charles welcome back we all missed you"! The restaurant manager says. "Chuck it's great to be back! When do I start"? The chef says to him. "Right fucking now"! Chuck says to him.

The clown smiles as he looks through the window lighting up another cigar and happy for his new apprentice. "Charles you're going to be alright buddy. I have a lot of faith in you". The clown said and then started walking down the street.

"Now I'm on my way to go help a plumber from killing his wife. Hopefully I can get there in time before the massacre happens"! The clown says as he laughs his ass off walking down the street leaving a smoke trail behind him from his cigar.

5/16/20

Good

Fuck the bullshit! Fuck'em. Who gives a fuck anyway? Most people in this world only give a fuck about what they want. To be blatantly honest and the real truth is the world doesn't give a fuck!

None of them do. What the fuck now and what the fuck happened?

The time has come to fucking prepare for war! Ten thousand tanks are armed and ready to destroy everything in their path. Unleash the hell from high above as the cargo planes drop a fuck ton of their bombs taking out the enemy below.

Fuck these politicians they care only about their own selfish needs. Do you honestly think they do all of this because they give flying fuck about us all? I don't think so. As a matter of fact I know that none of these politicians will never ever give two flying shits about us! And most likely none of them ever will.

January 22, 1987 Mr. Robert Budd Dwyer he learn the fucking hard way on that day. "Quick someone get a doctor"! One man screams in the crowd. I say good as that motherfucker bleeds out through his nose. Fuck him! I can honestly say it now as that no good swindling trickster burns in hell.

Fuck Mr. know it all! What the hell do these assholes really know anyway? Nobody on this planet has the answers to everything. I sure as fuck don't have all of the answers either.

Fuck those demons that try to poison the human minds. What good does it do? Nothing! Holy fuck that was good, winning the lottery and most of the problems go away but for how long?

Did you die? No. Good! Then shut the fuck up! Once again fuck the bullshit! Fuck the pain. Gain all that you can while you still have the time. Run through all of those motherfuckers that stand in your way.

Come on you can do it. Say it with me now. Fuck it all. Good!

1/4/20

Five

Take the bad equally with the good. There are too many things to bitch and cry over in life itself. Even if our commander and chief takes a sloppy shit on the carpet while he barks orders at us and the rest of the world, trust me it can always be far worse.

But yet the good will always light up the darkness. However in some moments there is not enough time. Sometimes it's too little too late and a shadow will cast itself to ruin the fucking day.

Trust me on this. No matter what the stress from life alone will kill even the strongest of us all. Never forget that we are all more human than human and we all come from the same blood stream.

Ten thousand children are screaming and crying at the top of their lungs as their eyes and ears start bleeding from the pressure building up. Oh don't worry. You can trust me because I understand. It's ok to press that long nose chrome 44 magnum against your fucking head! That's right. End it all and the pain goes away forever. Problem solved!

Your wife just got pregnant by the neighbor. While your dog takes a shit on the floor. The truck payment is due and it's falling apart. Josh your sixteen year son just smoked the last of your weed and drank the last case of beer. To top it all off you're 58,903.67 in debt.

Now don't lose your shit just yet. Believe me, hang there. Don't you trust me by now? I have the perfect solution to fix this never ending fucking problem!

Just count to five. That's right! One, two, three, four and five!

Congratulations every single living thing on this planet is now all five seconds closer to death! Feel better now?

3/4/20

Beautify Insane

Fuck that sunrise. A supercharged heaven to jump start the madness of the day. Hit the clutch and shift it back into reverse. Spin that motherfucker around in a 360 onto the black ice!

Within an instant she cracks opens another beer while the sounds of Griz and Snails blast through the 1,000 watt subwoofers in the background. Now she drives through hell on earth with a massive drop of heaven coating every single brain cell she has.

It's time to show those demons your perfect smile as you pass them all by. Smile now sweetie darling as you take them all on.

It's ok to love the pain! It makes everything a motherfucking vacation. An unstoppable force of a juggernaut! Again remember life is this, it's filled with some good and the rest of it is a bunch of motherfucking bullshit and pain!

A blood soaked head banging massacre. A blue haired goddess giving smurf jobs while lasers fire out of her eyes as this massive Jedi flip takes over!

This lady does a triple back flip with two liquid swords in her hands. Then she lands on the floor doing a full split but with lightening reflexes she jumps up with a spinning side kick and breaks his glass jaw instantaneously.

If anyone talks shit or disrespects the great legend this blue haired beauty will correct that problem by splitting their skulls wide open with a baseball bat. "You will love my Fred forever"! She screams as the blood, brains and eye balls fly all over the fucking place! A new found power overcomes her while this bloody mess covers her face!

No second thoughts. The rolling behind her closed eye lids is electrifying fast! Don't stop now you sexy ass blue haired bitch, now hit the fucking gas and drive that tank of a truck straight through that police barricade. Smile now babe for the world is yours as you paint it all purple and green!

Turn it up louder than ever before! Who gives a fuck about what they think. Take them all on with that perfect beautiful smile of yours. Most of all never hold back!

While the thunder roars in the background you fire up that joint. Fly fast down this highway doing 300mph. As you're inside this customized

Hennessey venom GT, you look back in your rear view mirror watching the storm closing in.

Rip the fucking lungs out of time to stop the countless bullshit from ever happening. Cut that dictators head off then kick its bloody corpse off the fucking throne!

A perfect genetically engineered psycho driven maniac mixed with a cluster fuck of addictive madness! But holy Christ within heaven and in hell those painted nails and cat like eyes still look perfect to me!

Shifting into the fourth and final gear of a 1969 Mustang GT 500 Shelby Cobra with an all wheel drive gripping the ground! You look behind you at the government building holding new highly advanced classified technology.

Quickly you push the red button detonating a massive amount of C4 to go off. A God like explosion fills the sky in a seductive horror. Meanwhile as the destruction takes place you scream out "Fuck those assholes, now let's break all of the fucking laws"! Thank you pretty sexy blue haired lady of psychedelic violence!

Candy flipping inside a hotel suite of Caesars palace in Las Vegas, you wrap a giant silver chain around that high rollers dick. Quickly you move that squirrely fuck closer to you with his hands tied behind his back.

"You are now my fucking servant"! You scream at him one inch away from his eyes. With no warning at all you force your long tongue down his throat and out of his asshole tickling his nut sack for ten seconds.

Smoothly fast your tongue comes back up his asshole and out of his mouth. With finesse you push him back with your right hand then you yank that chain in your left hand. Here comes the over right hook. Bam, right in the nose breaking it into a bloody horrific thrilling mess!

"I told you, you're going to be my fucking servant. Now give me whatever I want or I will turn your little wife into my fucking whore"! You scream at him as he is now on the floor with his dick hard as rock hard meanwhile your eyes transform into souls of black!

Holy motherfucking blue ball Christmas! I love the fact that you are a sexy ass wild thing ready to break bones with two fingers. Light up the first cigarette at dawn, get a downlink tattoo and get both of your holes licked from a two tongue long black haired slut!

As another day begins again you always stand tall holding the weight of the world. I don't give two flying fucking squirts of piss what they say about you, to me you will forever be beautifully insane!

3/25/20

Extreme Force of an Adrenaline Head Rush

Shove your seven foot dick straight up the Queen's twat and out of her mouth just to take a filthy piss straight down this fucking dictator's throat as he tries to preach that bullshit to the masses.

The weak and the strong minded ones, take them both one by one. Push them all into an unholy God forsaken piss blood bath, motherfucking speed racing cluster fuck nut world of pure perfection.

That's right! Fuck it, I'm going to kick this one into high gear! Grab a hold of the, oh shit bar and let's go for a ride kids!

Enforce the unforeseen pain. Drive that fist full of nails straight into the abyss of a hellish nightmare! Crack open the minds of the insane. But there's nothing to fucking worry about while their talents consists of pissing perfect creativity all over the hospital walls!

A slack jaw jack ass who thinks he fucking knows it all. However little miss eighteen year old Tiffany just knows how to grab a hold of his hairy nut sack and make that fuck obey her every sick, twisted, psycho wet command!

The all knowing and never ending, but I do know this. No matter how sexy and perfect she looks within twelve hours or less. This perfect ten is going to take the shit of her life right after she drinks a mixture of a hundred ounces of prune juice and turbo lax!

Mechanical animals high as a motherfucker on psychedelic medications are running loose through Disney World! Don't panic and nothing to fear for they will help spin your lovely child a million times on the merry go round.

As your spoil little shit of a brat screams in horror going faster and faster. Finally that little fuck pukes a rainbow of lucky charms all over the great American dream!

Dance with the devil? I don't think so. Fuck his little napoleon ass! I'll drain that sucker's blood and transform it into bloody Marys for the strippers in titty city to drink. When the peak hits them just the right way they will hallucinate demonic images across the planet!

Maniac veins are open and waiting for the extreme force of an adrenaline head rush! Oh fuck yes indeed 1,000 grams of chronic rig smoke fills the house up with the windows locked so there's no escape!

Rolling your milk filled tits off as you jump out of the helicopter with no parachute, but everything is going to be fine, for a hundred midget clowns are waiting for you below with a net. At the same time there eyes are wide open from being high as a motherfucker on mescaline and crystal meth!

Holy bleeding assholes here comes the King ready to split heads wide open and create a new fucking sloppy wet dream. As for the Queen she is conquering the new lands building her own kingdom filled with bath houses, drug dealers, drag strips, killing fields, and a night club called face down bottoms up!

Mega man and the Iron man are sending nuclear atomic blasts to eradicate the pure evil of this land. Meanwhile batman takes out five hundred shadow ninjas with stealth speed and state of the art weapons.

The time has come and you cannot stop it! A drunk that's out of control driving a 1,000 horse power Go kart who is also your seventy year grandfather straight through the mall. Then the old bastard screams out "Fuck you assholes, I'm retired"! As he laughs his ass off and drives straight through the glass doors of Macy's.

Finally the tiger disobeys and jumps on the magician ripping apart and taking off his arm. This definitely puts a smile on my face as I inhale nitrous oxide balloons while that stupid fuck screams in pain and agony in front of the entire audience. I say great! Fuck him and I hope the tiger rips off even more of him.

The sounds of a hundred mega ton nuclear war head going off at 5:00AM helps wake me up to take the first piss of the day. The incredible grabs a hold of an asteroid and smashes it into a planet. Pulverizing and annihilating this place called home to billions into obliteration!

Seven billion assholes worldwide are ready to take the shit of their lives every day. Here's a new quote for you. A clean asshole is always a great way to start the day!

An indestructible machine has been taken over the world from the mind of a twelve year social path of a monster. This little bastard shows no mercy. Hydro planning through the lake with your mistress on your shoulders, a joint in your mouth, a fifth of grey goose in her hand and you balance each other by holding the handle with your dick wrapped around it.

The end of the beginning, but I haven't even pushed through the fucking boundaries yet. It's now time to go to the dark side. Two minutes until death grabs a hold of your soul. Scream at the top of your lungs as you spit that fire from the heavens above!

Split that bitch's tongue in two so she can jerk off twice the amount of cock with her new gifted talents. This way she can make twice the profit. Fuck that legion of demons! I will unleash and send in the Goddess's after them to cut their heads off, rip out their hearts and eat them for breakfast. While they come up with new plots to take over the world! Fuck yes! Sleazy Talesey has done it again!

All of these advanced weapon systems across this planet cannot stop this chaotic monster created from a God! This creation is known as the human race. That's right people we are the psychopaths of the universe and I fucking love it!

Trillions of thoughts will bounce around inside your own mind with the speed of a pinball machine. This will take place after three hours of taking a massive amount of candy flipping! Let's throw in some nitrous balloons just to help with the thinking process.

Obey the laws! Oh yeah! I have a better idea. You over there please help me create this new beast and lets transform that giant police station into luxury whore house, strip club, shopping mall, pet store, casino, spa, day care, bar & grill.

500,000 watts of bass fills this place with ground breaking vibes, like a perfect earthquake while the strippers head bang and dance around like never before. These lovely ladies have been drinking nothing but expensive vodka and gin. It definitely makes this once a police station the perfect getaway from life's stressful situations.

Here's the added bonus there's free liquid LSD shooting out of the tits from a statue of an angel praising to the good lord and savior! But have no fear like the hatter once said. "We are all a little mad here".

As we stand back and you look at this perfect monster of a creation, I want you to yell out. "Hi Mom and Dad look at what I have created. This is the best I can do and fuck isn't not half bad"!

I might be going to hell in a red stingray. But thankfully my perfect whore of a wife and her twin sister are swallowing all of the cum from every dick in the neighborhood! No time for forgiveness. Just drive and force the adrenaline into your mind until the pressure blows out the back of your skull!

A fuck ton of thunderous sounds in the dark and the infinite lightning strikes all around. Today is an excellent day for an exorcism! Cannabis roots intertwine around the skull of a Texas longhorn. Begging for hours just to have one little taste of her, but this bitch won't let you have any of it!

That's right slippery sweetness just allow the takeover to come over and I promise you'll be walking a straight line the next morning.

Throwing stones, knives, axes, swords, meat cleavers, darts and even ice picks at her while she spins around on a giant wheel colored black, purple, red and pink. But here's the catch, there's a two foot joint hanging out of her mouth and a one foot bong attached to her pussy inhaling that thick white chronic smoke. Yes! A stoned out, high as a motherfucker hello kitty brings out the joker smile in me every time!

Millions of heat seeking missiles takes out these miss behaving psycho driven maniac humans. I just want to see the violence unfold in a meaningful and positive way! Please let me know if this is too much to ask from you brilliant fucking people?

Get lit! Dissect that insect just to find out what fuck makes it tick. The walls are melting from the psilocybin effects. The alcoholic soaked mind is now awake as you shift into four wheel drive hiking up the mountain as you drag your mother in law behind!

Psycho driven hamsters on dirt bikes are racing through six flags great adventure carrying sixty caliber sub machine guns taking all of the parent's money. Just before they leave all the kids get free rides, food and drinks for the day. Now this is what I call social justice at its finest!

Cheap thrills, a crooked look in his eye! A slap across the fucking mouth please. DMT electrical has finally arrived with clouds of smoke pouring out of the driver's side door. The psycho whores have finally taken over hell. Now they're all taking turns beating the living shit out of that two horned fuck called Satan with a sledge hammer. And now they're fucking him up his bleeding asshole with it!

Psilocybin, morning glory, Iboga, DMT oh yes indeed LSD! Never forget about the MDMA and cannabis. Tripping balls to the motherfucking inner walls!

The wife who is now filled perverted anger wearing a purple strap on has your babysitter bent over with a leash around her neck. "You let my husband get you pregnant you stupid little fucking whore"! "I'm sorry mistress; I promise it will never happen again". The little whore says. "You are not sorry yet"!

Choose your weapon. As for me I'll take the X! With eyes blacker than nights into the deep abyss I run into the darkness screaming "Fuck yes"! And now the abstract laser vision finally kicks in.

Help the young and the old. But the 28 year old who begs and complains, take him to edge of the bridge. Scream out loud with your eyes wide open showing your teeth "Let's have some real fucking fun. Hopefully we don't die"! Time to jump for the thrill of a lifetime, no turning back now! My

God this is beyond perfection as you both jump off hoping for a miracle to happen just before the impact happens! On the way down you scream out loud "Aren't you having fucking fun yet"?

I'm about ready to erase this whole book and start it all over again. But you know what fuck it! I'll just write the sequel instead. Come on children of all ages. It's time to bang your heads against these walls destroying this building from the inside out! I will soak and infect your minds with the dreams you want so bad to become real. But yet, these dreams were created from the nightmares you have in your sleep at night. Waking up at night yelling "Oh God, please help me"!

I am the fucking law! You will obey all that I say. I don't think so. In fact let's cut the funding to Mr. knows it all. Throw him into a dark hole for hundred days with no food or drink. That's right good luck asshole! Now over throw the government, create a new one, and legalize the psychedelics. Oh what a wonderful world this would be!

Kelly who is nineteen years old finally comes home early one morning. Hopefully she didn't forget to take her fucking birth control again! Because Kelly had a fucking bad ass time last night! Oh yes I promise she did.

My God even at 8am Monday morning she is still rolling her little hairless cunt off. Kelly is wearing nothing but fishnets, body paint, candy bracelets a thong and her hair looks like rainbow bright high on Aahuasca! The eye quakes are still spinning fast as she sticks out her pierced tongue.

Holy shitty titty this girl had a blast at the Rezz and Zeds Dead show last night! But now her father is awake and getting ready for work. He's in the kitchen looking at his daughter with pure hate and disgust while drinking his coffee. Father points his finger at her with strict and violent anger.

As the screaming begins, spit and coffee comes flying out his mouth showing his gap toothed grin. Father yells at his daughter "You are fucking out of control"!

5/30/20

The Author

Well hello there children of all ages. Oh yes indeed it is me talking to you right now. Look I know this book has been the most insane, repulsive, unpredictable, cluster fuck of perfection that I have created so far.

However let me take the time to be serious and say this. Please do not jump off a cliff to kill yourself, transforming into your spirit animal. To be honest the chances are very slim this will ever happen. Please and I cannot stress this one enough. But please be care on whatever psychedelic medications including cannabis or any drugs. Why you might ask because everybody is different.

Please don't hurt or kill one another. Remember everybody matters worldwide but this only my opinion. Please treat people with kindness and respect, especially towards women and the little clowns. I apologize to anyone out who is offended from what I have written especially women.

Look what I have written is some truth but most of all it's an extreme form of entertainment. I know not everyone is going to like my work and that's ok. For everyone else who loves what I do, I can never thank you enough.

Please believe me when I tell you all that I never wrote any of this type of material to piss off anyone. Or to make any of you upset or feel uncomfortable. I just want to push the fucking limits to the max without getting locked up, that's all. Besides I love pushing the fucking limits for the thrill of a shock value!
$$$$$$$$$$$$$$$$$$$$$$$$$$$$$

Soon the sequel will eventually come out. Just hang in there and give it some time. I promise the next one will become more graphic and unpredictable than what you just experienced.

Printed in Great Britain
by Amazon

27097398R00057